Volume 2

SAXOPHONE SOLOS
E♭ Alto with piano accompaniment
Editor: Paul Harvey

INDEX

CHESTER MUSIC

DANCE OF JOB'S COMFORTERS

VAUGHAN WILLIAMS

Used by kind permission of Oxford University Press, London

© Copyright for all countries 1977, 1990

Chester Music Limited

CH 55121

"THE SUN AND I"

SULLIVAN

MENUET

J.S. BACH

BADINERIE

J.S. BACH

ALLEGRO

ALLEGRO

LONDON'S BURNING

TOLMERS VILLAGE

COLIN COWLES

CAPRICE ANGLAIS

PAUL HARVEY

D.C. al Coda

NOTES

1. ## Dance of Job's Comforters
   ### Ralph Vaughan Williams (1872 - 1958)

   A famous saxophone solo from *Job: A Masque for Dancing*, in which Satan introduces three wily hypocrites who alternately pretend to comfort and revile the long-suffering Job.

2. ## "The Sun and I"   Sir Arthur Sullivan (1842 - 1900)

   An expressive melody from *The Mikado;* one of the ever popular operettas which Sullivan wrote in collaboration with W. S. Gilbert.

3. & 4. ## Menuet and Bandinerie
   ### Johann Sebastian Bach (1685 - 1750)

   Two movements from Bach's *Suite in B minor* for Flute and Strings.

5. ## Allegro   George Frederic Handel (1685 - 1759)

   Although much of Handel's oboe and flute music transcribes very well for saxophone, this Allegro, one of *Seven Pieces for Keyboard*, is particularly suited to the instrument.

6. ## London's Burning   Dorothy Harvey

   A new treatment, in irregular metre, of an old round.

7. ## Tolmers Village   Colin Cowles

   A saxophone version, by the composer, of his theme music for a television production of that name.

8. ## Caprice Anglais   Paul Harvey

   The Editor has the last word, with an Englishman's version of the ebullient style characteristic of French saxophone writing.